ARTHUR BLISS

Pastoral

for clarinet and piano

composed c. 1916

One of two pieces for clarinet and piano,
the other being *Rhapsody* which is unpublished
and whereabouts unknown.

Order No: Nov 120509

NOVELLO PUBLISHING LIMITED

Cat. No. 12 0509 09

PASTORAL
for Clarinet in A (or B♭) and Piano

Duration 8'30"

ARTHUR BLISS

Permission to perform this work in public must be obtained from The Performing Right Society Limited, 29/33 Berners Street, London W1P 4AA or from the affiliated Society overseas.

20258

4

Novello & Company Limited

20258A

Printed in Great Britain

PASTORAL
for Clarinet in A (or Bb) and Piano

CLARINET in Bb

ARTHUR BLISS

Cat. No. 12 0509 09
© Novello & Company Limited 1980

20258A
All Rights Reserved

PASTORAL
for Clarinet in A (or B♭) and Piano

CLARINET in A

ARTHUR BLISS

Cat. No. 12 0509 09

© Novello & Company Limited 1980

20258A

All Rights Reserved

Novello & Company Limited

Printed in Great Britain

1/94 (16954)